FUN WITH PEANUTS

FUN WITH

Selected Cartoons from
GOOD OL' CHARLIE BROWN
(Volume 1)

PEANUTS

by Charles M. Schulz

A FAWCETT CREST BOOK

FAWCETT PUBLICATIONS, INC., GREENWICH, CONN.
MEMBER OF AMERICAN BOOK PUBLISHERS COUNCIL, INC.

Other Peanuts Books in Fawcett Crest Editions

Only 50¢ Each—Wherever Paperbacks Are Sold

FUN WITH PEANUTS

This book, prepared especially for Fawcett Publications, Inc., comprises the first half of GOOD OL' CHARLIE BROWN, and is reprinted by arrangement with Holt, Rinehart and Winston, Inc.

Sixteenth Fawcett Crest printing, February 1969

Published by Fawcett World Library,
67 West 44th Street, New York, New York 10036.
Printed in the United States of America.

YOU FASCINATE ME!

SCHULZ

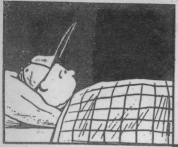

MONDAY IS OUR FIRST GAME, AND I'M SCARED TO DEATH..

WHAT A TEAM I'VE GOT... FIVE BOYS, THREE GIRLS AND A DOG! GOOD GRIEF!!

I DON'T KNOW WHY I EVER TRIED TO BE A MANAGER..I MUST BE OUT OF MY MIND!

I WONDER IF CASEY STENGEL IS ASLEEP?

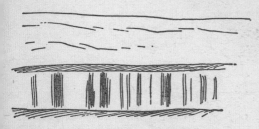

SCHULZ

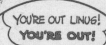

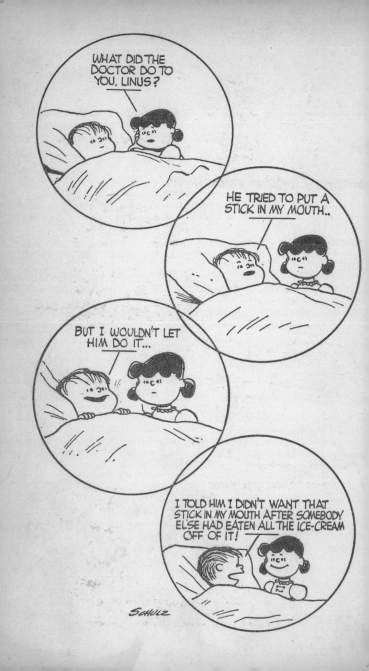

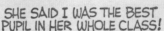

LET'S GO INSIDE AND WATCH TELEVISION...

I'M BEGINNING TO FEEL INSIGNIFICANT..

Billy and Susie are twins. They live in the city.

Here is their house. It is white. Here is their car. It is red.

In the morning Father goes to work. Mother cleans the house. The children play in the yard.

HERE'S A BOOK I THINK MAYBE YOU'LL LIKE, CHARLIE BROWN... IT GIVES A FASCINATING DESCRIPTION OF LIFE IN THE CITY!

SCHULZ

SHUDDER!

HE WAS EATING ANIMAL CRACKERS AND.. AND...AND.. **SMILING!!**

SCHULZ.

I THOUGHT I TOLD YOU TO STOP THAT DANCING?! YOU HAVE NO RIGHT TO BE SO HAPPY!!! NOW, STOP IT! DO YOU HEAR ME?!

SCHULZ

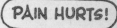

SCHULZ

I'VE BEEN WATCHING THESE BUGS, CHARLIE BROWN...

YOU SEE, THIS ONE BUG HERE IS ABOUT TO LEAVE HOME.. HE'S BEEN SAYING GOOD-BYE TO ALL HIS FRIENDS

SUDDENLY, THIS LITTLE GIRL BUG COMES RUNNING UP, AND TRIES TO PERSUADE HIM NOT TO LEAVE...

IF YOU'RE GOING TO BE A GOOD 'BUG-WATCHER', YOU HAVE TO HAVE LOTS OF IMAGINATION!

SCHULZ